Spelling is part of Primary English whether they like it or not

'Spelling Superstar or Spelling Swamp Dweller' works by setting clear targets. We think kids do better if they know exactly what they're being asked to do...

AT LEAST 50% OF SPELLINGS MUST BE CORRECT BY THE END OF THE YEAR

...and this book gives kids lots of practice to make sure they do.

Here's how it works...

1) Make sure the whole class knows that:
   - the point of this book is to BE A SPELLING SUPERSTAR
   - you stay a Superstar by meeting targets
   - to do well in primary English you must get at least 50% of spellings right

2) We've left a space for you to write a target at the top of each page, e.g. 5/20 or 25%.

3) Targets should get tougher over the year.

4) If a child meets their target, they're a Superstar, but if they miss one they become a Swamp Dweller — until next time they meet their targets.

5) Then you can circle the Superstar or Swamp Dweller at the top of each page.

6) Even better, make a massive poster, with stickers for the kids' names. Move the names from Superstar to Swamp Dweller in a weekly ceremony. Give prizes for becoming a Superstar, and punishments for becoming a Swamp Dweller — may we suggest running round the school waving their hands in the air shouting, "I've got smelly pants and I don't care!" or doing the page again for homework.

un and dis

Copy out the words once, cover with the flap and write them again.
Get _____ right to become a Spelling Superstar.

Read	Copy	Cover
1) unwell	1	1
2) untidy	2	2
3) unpick	3	3
4) unzip	4	4
5) unhappy	5	5
6) unseen	6	6
7) unable	7	7
8) unlucky	8	8
9) unpopular	9	9
10) unusual	10	10
11) dislike	11	11
12) disobey	12	12
13) disagree	13	13
14) dislodge	14	14
15) dishonest	15	15
16) disappear	16	16
17) displease	17	17
18) disqualify	18	18
19) dishearten	19	19
20) disembark	20	20

BONUS QUESTION		
E1) disinfect	E1	E1

un and dis

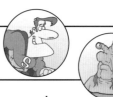

Put the flap over the last page and use the hints to work out the words.
Get _____ right to become a Spelling Superstar.

Hint hint

1) Not well.

2) Messy.

3) U _ p _ c _ the stitches.

4) U _ z _ p your coat.

5) Sad.

6) Not seen.

7) Not able.

8) Bad luck.

9) Opposite of popular.

10) Different.

11) Don't like.

12) Break the rules.

13) Have a different opinion.

14) It was hard to d _ slo _ g _.

15) Telling lies.

16) Suddenly not there.

17) Annoy.

18) Chuck out for cheating.

19) Lose heart.

20) Get off a ship.

One last time...

1 ....

2 ....

3 ....

4 ....

5 ....

6 ....

7 ....

8 ....

9 ....

10 ....

11 ....

12 ....

13 ....

14 ....

15 ....

16 ....

17 ....

18 ....

19 ....

20 ....

BONUS QUESTION

E1) Cover in disinfectant.

E1 ....

de, re and pre

Copy out the words once, cover with the flap and write them again.
Get _____ right to become a Spelling Superstar.

© CGP 2002

Read	Copy	Cover
1) demist	1	1
2) de-ice	2	2
3) decode	3	3
4) defuse	4	4
5) debug	5	5
6) deform	6	6
7) decompose	7	7
8) refill	8	8
9) repay	9	9
10) rebuild	10	10
11) rebound	11	11
12) retreat	12	12
13) replace	13	13
14) recede	14	14
15) prefix	15	15
16) prepare	16	16
17) predict	17	17
18) previous	18	18
19) preface	19	19
20) premature	20	20

BONUS QUESTION		
E1) precaution	E1	E1

de, re and pre

Put the flap over the last page and use the hints to work out the words.
Get _____ right to become a Spelling Superstar.

Hint hint	One last time...
1) Get the mist off.	1
2) Get the ice off.	2
3) Break a code.	3
4) Make a bomb harmless.	4
5) Remove computer errors.	5
6) Make ugly.	6
7) Rot.	7
8) Fill up again.	8
9) Pay money back.	9
10) Build again.	10
11) Bounce back.	11
12) To back away from something.	12
13) I must r _ p _ ace my old hat.	13
14) Go slowly backwards.	14
15) Bit added to the start of words.	15
16) Make ready.	16
17) Guess the future.	17
18) The one before.	18
19) Notes at the beginning of a book.	19
20) Too early.	20

BONUS QUESTION	
E1) Protecting yourself in advance.	E1

© CGP 2002

Year Three Spelling — Word Beginnings

mis and non

Copy out the words once, cover with the flap and write them again.
Get _____ right to become a Spelling Superstar.

Read	Copy	Cover
1) mistake	1	1
2) mishear	2	2
3) misread	3	3
4) misplace	4	4
5) misbehave	5	5
6) misdeal	6	6
7) misfire	7	7
8) miscount	8	8
9) miscalculate	9	9
10) misfortune	10	10
11) misconduct	11	11
12) non-stop	12	12
13) non-drip	13	13
14) non-stick	14	14
15) nonsense	15	15
16) non-smoker	16	16
17) non-starter	17	17
18) non-violent	18	18
19) non-fiction	19	19
20) non-believer	20	20

BONUS QUESTION		
E1) misinform	E1	E1

mis and non

Put the flap over the last page and use the hints to work out the words.
Get _____ right to become a Spelling Superstar.

Hint hint	One last time...
1) Error.	1
2) Hear something wrongly.	2
3) Read something wrongly.	3
4) Put in the wrong place.	4
5) Behave badly.	5
6) Deal cards wrongly.	6
7) Go wrong.	7
8) Counting the wrong number.	8
9) Get a sum wrong.	9
10) Another word for 'bad luck'.	10
11) Bad behaviour.	11
12) Without end.	12
13) No drips.	13
14) Like all good frying pans.	14
15) Rubbish.	15
16) Opposite of a smoker.	16
17) Idea that doesn't work.	17
18) Other word for 'peaceful'.	18
19) Opposite of fiction.	19
20) Someone who doesn't believe.	20

BONUS QUESTION

E1) Give incorrect information.	E1

ex, co and anti

Copy out the words once, cover with the flap and write them again.

Get _____ right to become a Spelling Superstar.

Read	Copy	Cover
1) exit	1	1
2) exile	2	2
3) expel	3	3
4) export	4	4
5) explode	5	5
6) extend	6	6
7) exclaim	7	7
8) exterior	8	8
9) exchange	9	9
10) excursion	10	10
11) co-star	11	11
12) co-write	12	12
13) co-operate	13	13
14) coincidence	14	14
15) coeducation	15	15
16) antidote	16	16
17) antibiotic	17	17
18) antifreeze	18	18
19) antiseptic	19	19
20) anticlockwise	20	20

BONUS QUESTION		
E 1) exotic	E1	E1

ex, co and anti

Put the flap over the last page and use the hints to work out the words.
Get _____ right to become a Spelling Superstar.

Hint hint	One last time...
1) The way out.	1
2) Someone who's been kicked out.	2
3) Push out.	3
4) Selling stuff to other countries.	4
5) Blow up.	5
6) Make bigger.	6
7) Yell out.	7
8) The outside.	8
9) I'll e _ cha _ g _ some money.	9
10) A day out.	10
11) Less famous actor in a movie.	11
12) Write something together.	12
13) All work together.	13
14) Happening by chance.	14
15) Schools with girls and boys.	15
16) The cure for poison.	16
17) A type of medicine.	17
18) Gets rid of frost on car windows.	18
19) Used to clean cuts.	19
20) The opposite of clockwise.	20

BONUS QUESTION

E1) Different from the norm.	E1

ing words

Copy out the words once, cover with the flap and write them again.
Get _____ right to become a Spelling Superstar.

Read	Copy	Cover
1) doing	1	1
2) going	2	2
3) helping	3	3
4) asking	4	4
5) meeting	5	5
6) spending	6	6
7) pulling	7	7
8) looking	8	8
9) trying	9	9
10) walking	10	10
11) jumping	11	11
12) enjoying	12	12
13) leading	13	13
14) watching	14	14
15) saying	15	15
16) begging	16	16
17) thinking	17	17
18) waiting	18	18
19) playing	19	19
20) talking	20	20

BONUS QUESTION		
E1) wanting	E1	E1

ing words

Put the flap over the last page and use the hints to work out the words.
Get _____ right to become a Spelling Superstar.

Hint hint	One last time...
1) A verb is a _ _ _ _ _ word.	1 ....
2) Jibba was g _ _ _ g to Spain.	2 ....
3) Lending a hand.	3 ....
4) Posing a question.	4 ....
5) M _ _ _ ing new friends.	5 ....
6) Using money to get new stuff.	6 ....
7) Opposite of pushing.	7 ....
8) Watching something.	8 ....
9) Having a go.	9 ....
10) Even slower than jogging.	10 ....
11) Ju _ _ ing for joy.	11 ....
12) Having a good time.	12 ....
13) Going at the front.	13 ....
14) Looking at something.	14 ....
15) Talking to someone.	15 ....
16) Please, please, please.	16 ....
17) Trying to find an answer.	17 ....
18) Wa _ _ ing for the bus.	18 ....
19) Messing around.	19 ....
20) Chatting to someone.	20 ....

BONUS QUESTION

E1) W _ _ t _ _ _ some presents.	E1 ....

ing words

Copy out the words once, cover with the flap and write them again.
Get _____ right to become a Spelling Superstar.

Read	Copy	Cover
1) taking	1	1
2) smiling	2	2
3) hating	3	3
4) making	4	4
5) driving	5	5
6) raising	6	6
7) hoping	7	7
8) caring	8	8
9) staring	9	9
10) amazing	10	10
11) hopping	11	11
12) running	12	12
13) clapping	13	13
14) rubbing	14	14
15) fitting	15	15
16) sitting	16	16
17) planning	17	17
18) slimming	18	18
19) chatting	19	19
20) tipping	20	20

BONUS QUESTION		
E1) beeping	E1	E1

ing words

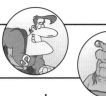

Put the flap over the last page and use the hints to work out the words.
Get _____ right to become a Spelling Superstar.

Hint hint	One last time...
1) Opposite of giving.	1
2) What's this guy doing? 🙂	2
3) Strong dislike.	3
4) Building something.	4
5) _ _ _ _ _ _ _ a car.	5
6) Lifting something higher.	6
7) Wanting something to happen.	7
8) Looking after something.	8
9) Looking for a long time.	9
10) Out of this world.	10
11) Jumping on one leg.	11
12) Faster than walking.	12
13) Slapping hands together.	13
14) Ru _ _ ing two sticks makes fire.	14
15) fi _ _ ing	15
16) _ _ _ _ _ _ _ cross-legged.	16
17) Thinking about what to do.	17
18) Losing weight.	18
19) Talking to someone.	19
20) Leaning something over.	20

BONUS QUESTION	
E1) Electronic noises.	E1

le words

Copy out the words once, cover with the flap and write them again.
Get _____ right to become a Spelling Superstar.

Read	Copy	Cover
1) tickle	1	1
2) pickle	2	2
3) chuckle	3	3
4) reliable	4	4
5) able	5	5
6) vegetable	6	6
7) guzzle	7	7
8) muddle	8	8
9) wobble	9	9
10) nozzle	10	10
11) nettle	11	11
12) paddle	12	12
13) uncle	13	13
14) cycle	14	14
15) circle	15	15
16) article	16	16
17) obstacle	17	17
18) miracle	18	18
19) cubicle	19	19
20) icicle	20	20

BONUS QUESTION		
E1) particle	E1	E1

le words

Put the flap over the last page and use the hints to work out the words.
Get _____ right to become a Spelling Superstar.

Hint hint	One last time...
1) A t _ _ kle makes you giggle.	1
2) Some p _ _ kle on sandwiches.	2
3) A sort of giggle.	3
4) Never goes wrong.	4
5) Can do that.	5
6) What your Mum makes you eat.	6
7) Drinking fast.	7
8) Getting things all confused.	8
9) Jiggling around.	9
10) The thing on the end of a hose.	10
11) Evil stinging plant.	11
12) Not quite swimming.	12
13) Your Dad's brother.	13
14) What you do on a bike.	14
15) A one-sided shape.	15
16) Writing in a newspaper.	16
17) Stuff that gets in your way.	17
18) Turning water into wine.	18
19) The walls around the toilet.	19
20) Pointy bits of ice.	20

BONUS QUESTION

E1) Everything is made of these.	E1

le words

Copy out the words once, cover with the flap and write them again.
Get _____ right to become a Spelling Superstar.

Read	Copy	Cover
1) candle	1	1
2) handle	2	2
3) needle	3	3
4) noodle	4	4
5) poodle	5	5
6) bundle	6	6
7) double	7	7
8) trouble	8	8
9) fable	9	9
10) tumble	10	10
11) rumble	11	11
12) bible	12	12
13) sensible	13	13
14) possible	14	14
15) horrible	15	15
16) terrible	16	16
17) example	17	17
18) dimple	18	18
19) crumple	19	19
20) apple	20	20

BONUS QUESTION		
E1) simple	E1	E1

le words

Put the flap over the last page and use the hints to work out the words.
Get _____ right to become a Spelling Superstar.

Hint hint

1) Made of wax and needs lighting.
2) Holding something in your hands.
3) The thing for sewing.
4) n _ _ dle
5) Silly dog with a funny haircut.
6) A b _ _ dle of sticks.
7) Not single but...
8) Get yourself into tr _ _ _ le.
9) A fairy tale.
10) A small fall.
11) Deep grumbling sound.
12) Big book about God.
13) sen _ _ _ le
14) Can definitely be done.
15) Nasty, yucky.
16) Not good at all.
17) ex _ _ _ le
18) di _ _ le
19) Crushing something.
20) Tasty fruit.

One last time...

1 ....
2 ....
3 ....
4 ....
5 ....
6 ....
7 ....
8 ....
9 ....
10 ....
11 ....
12 ....
13 ....
14 ....
15 ....
16 ....
17 ....
18 ....
19 ....
20 ....

BONUS QUESTION

E1) Very easy.

E1 ....

er and est

Copy out the words once, cover with the flap and write them again.
Get _____ right to become a Spelling Superstar.

Read	Copy	Cover
1) nicer	1	1
2) nicest	2	2
3) smarter	3	3
4) smartest	4	4
5) faster	5	5
6) fastest	6	6
7) cold	7	7
8) colder	8	8
9) tall	9	9
10) tallest	10	10
11) quick	11	11
12) quicker	12	12
13) wise	13	13
14) wisest	14	14
15) happy	15	15
16) happier	16	16
17) funny	17	17
18) funniest	18	18
19) crazy	19	19
20) crazier	20	20

BONUS QUESTION		
E1) luckiest	E1	E1

er and est

Put the flap over the last page and use the hints to work out the words.
Get _____ right to become a Spelling Superstar.

Hint hint	One last time...
1) Better than the last thing.	1 ....
2) ni _ _ st	2 ....
3) Cleverer than others.	3 ....
4) The cleverest of them all.	4 ....
5) Quicker than others.	5 ....
6) The quickest.	6 ....
7) Not warm.	7 ....
8) Even less warm.	8 ....
9) Opposite of short.	9 ....
10) The biggest of them all.	10 ....
11) Another word for fast.	11 ....
12) Another word for faster.	12 ....
13) Knowing a lot of things.	13 ....
14) Person who knows the most.	14 ....
15) Don't worry, be h _ _ _ y.	15 ....
16) hap _ _ _ r	16 ....
17) Jokes that make you smile are...	17 ....
18) The best joke is the f _ _ niest.	18 ....
19) A bit bonkers.	19 ....
20) cr _ _ _ er	20 ....

BONUS QUESTION

E1) The most lucky.	E1 ....

Words that end in y

Copy out the words once, cover with the flap and write them again.
Get _____ right to become a Spelling Superstar.

Read	Copy	Cover
1) funny	1	1
2) fatty	2	2
3) furry	3	3
4) runny	4	4
5) nutty	5	5
6) sunny	6	6
7) crispy	7	7
8) smelly	8	8
9) cheeky	9	9
10) watery	10	10
11) fussy	11	11
12) fully	12	12
13) greasy	13	13
14) hazy	14	14
15) lazy	15	15
16) bony	16	16
17) smoky	17	17
18) stony	18	18
19) scary	19	19
20) slimy	20	20

BONUS QUESTION		
E1) scratchy	E1	E1

Words that end in y

Put the flap over the last page and use the hints to work out the words.
Get _____ right to become a Spelling Superstar.

Hint hint	One last time...
1) Jokes are this.	1 ....
2) Food with lots of fat in it.	2 ....
3) Dogs and cats are this.	3 ....
4) A cold gives you a _____ nose.	4 ....
5) Containing lots of nuts.	5 ....
6) If it's not cloudy it's _____.	6 ....
7) This bacon is very _____.	7 ....
8) Pooh! A bad pong.	8 ....
9) Being rude and cocky.	9 ....
10) Lots of wet stuff.	10 ....
11) Being very choosy.	11 ....
12) Completely.	12 ....
13) Mechanics get like this.	13 ....
14) A blurry sky.	14 ....
15) Not getting up to do anything.	15 ....
16) So skinny you look all knobbly.	16 ....
17) Fires make the air like this.	17 ....
18) Difficult to walk on with bare feet.	18 ....
19) Frightening.	19 ....
20) Like a frog's back.	20 ....

BONUS QUESTION

E1) Prickly and itchy.	E1 ....

Plurals

Copy out the words once, cover with the flap and write them again.
Get _____ right to become a Spelling Superstar.

Read	Copy	Cover
1) tables	1	1
2) pens	2	2
3) tunes	3	3
4) lips	4	4
5) desks	5	5
6) toys	6	6
7) donkeys	7	7
8) rays	8	8
9) beans	9	9
10) shoes	10	10
11) times	11	11
12) boys	12	12
13) girls	13	13
14) crisps	14	14
15) cups	15	15
16) delays	16	16
17) computers	17	17
18) pockets	18	18
19) schools	19	19
20) ropes	20	20

BONUS QUESTION		
E1) flowers	E1	E1

Plurals

Put the flap over the last page and use the hints to work out the words.
Get _____ right to become a Spelling Superstar.

Hint hint	One last time...
1) Lots of these:	1 ....
2) Ink things you write with.	2 ....
3) You hum along to them.	3 ....
4) They move when you speak.	4 ....
5) You work on them at school.	5 ....
6) You play with these.	6 ....
7) Like horses but smaller.	7 ....
8) Sunlight comes down in these.	8 ....
9) Baked ____ are my favourite.	9 ....
10) These things:	10 ....
11) A word for '×' in maths.	11 ....
12) Young men.	12 ....
13) Young women.	13 ....
14) You eat them from a packet. SALT & VINEGAR	14 ....
15) You drink from them.	15 ....
16) Long _____ make you late.	16 ....
17) Machines you play games on.	17 ....
18) These things:	18 ....
19) Place where you go to learn.	19 ....
20) Use them for climbing things.	20 ....

BONUS QUESTION

E1) These things:	E1 ....

Plurals

Copy out the words once, cover with the flap and write them again.
Get _____ right to become a Spelling Superstar.

Read	Copy	Cover
1) foxes	1	1
2) sandwiches	2	2
3) ashes	3	3
4) brushes	4	4
5) glasses	5	5
6) inches	6	6
7) witches	7	7
8) dishes	8	8
9) churches	9	9
10) boxes	10	10
11) pennies	11	11
12) armies	12	12
13) jellies	13	13
14) puppies	14	14
15) parties	15	15
16) berries	16	16
17) flies	17	17
18) rubies	18	18
19) skies	19	19
20) spies	20	20

BONUS QUESTION		
E1) switches	E1	E1

Plurals

Put the flap over the last page and use the hints to work out the words.
Get _____ right to become a Spelling Superstar.

Hint hint	One last time...
1) Red, dog-like things.	1 ....
2) What you put in a lunch box.	2 ....
3) The stuff that's left after a fire.	3 ....
4) These things:	4 ....
5) Wear them to see properly.	5 ....
6) An old measurement of length.	6 ....
7) They ride on broomsticks.	7 ....
8) You eat off these.	8 ....
9) People pray in them.	9 ....
10) These things:	10 ....
11) Smallest value coins.	11 ....
12) Soldiers belong to them.	12 ....
13) They are all wobbly and yummy.	13 ....
14) Baby dogs.	14 ....
15) You have them on birthdays.	15 ....
16) They grow on holly bushes.	16 ....
17) They buzz around.	17 ....
18) Red gemstones.	18 ....
19) Planes fly through them.	19 ....
20) People like James Bond.	20 ....

BONUS QUESTION

E1) Use them to turn on lights.	E1 ....

ly and ful

Copy out the words once, cover with the flap and write them again.
Get _____ right to become a Spelling Superstar.

Read	Copy	Cover
1) kindly	1	1
2) friendly	2	2
3) actually	3	3
4) weekly	4	4
5) likely	5	5
6) really	6	6
7) carefully	7	7
8) properly	8	8
9) personally	9	9
10) especially	10	10
11) wishful	11	11
12) hopeful	12	12
13) successful	13	13
14) pitiful	14	14
15) merciful	15	15
16) resentful	16	16
17) painful	17	17
18) sorrowful	18	18
19) forgetful	19	19
20) needful	20	20

BONUS QUESTION		
E1) eventually	E1	E1

ly and ful

Put the flap over the last page and use the hints to work out the words.

Get _____ right to become a Spelling Superstar.

Hint hint	One last time...
1) A good person.	1 ....
2) Nice and likeable.	2 ....
3) I'm not 7, I'm _____ 7½.	3 ....
4) Every 7 days.	4 ....
5) It's very _____ to happen.	5 ....
6) I'm 102, I'm _____ old.	6 ....
7) Done with care.	7 ....
8) Doing things the right way.	8 ....
9) Doing it yourself.	9 ....
10) In particular.	10 ....
11) Wishing for something.	11 ....
12) Hoping for something.	12 ....
13) Doing what you set out to do.	13 ....
14) A pathetic person.	14 ....
15) Having mercy.	15 ....
16) Being jealous.	16 ....
17) It hurts.	17 ....
18) Full of sorrow.	18 ....
19) Not being able to remember.	19 ....
20) Needing something.	20 ....

BONUS QUESTION	
E1) In the end.	E1 ....

less and able

Copy out the words once, cover with the flap and write them again.
Get _____ right to become a Spelling Superstar.

Read	Copy	Cover
1) careless	1	1
2) thoughtless	2	2
3) homeless	3	3
4) jobless	4	4
5) thankless	5	5
6) fearless	6	6
7) headless	7	7
8) endless	8	8
9) speechless	9	9
10) lifeless	10	10
11) reliable	11	11
12) drinkable	12	12
13) enjoyable	13	13
14) avoidable	14	14
15) readable	15	15
16) arguable	16	16
17) probable	17	17
18) breakable	18	18
19) touchable	19	19
20) sinkable	20	20

BONUS QUESTION

E1) merciless	E1	E1

© CGP 2002

less and able

Put the flap over the last page and use the hints to work out the words.
Get _____ right to become a Spelling Superstar.

Hint hint	*One last time...*
1) Not careful.	1
2) Not thinking of others.	2
3) Being without a home. 	3
4) Not having a job.	4
5) A job nobody will thank you for.	5
6) Not being scared of anything.	6
7) Without a head.	7
8) Never-ending.	8
9) Being lost for words.	9
10) Something dead and limp.	10
11) You can rely on them.	11
12) Orange juice is this.	12
13) Something that's good fun.	13
14) You can miss it out.	14
15) The Harry Potter books are this.	15
16) It's not clearly a fact.	16
17) It likely.	17
18) Easily smashable.	18
19) You can pick it up.	19
20) You can make it sink.	20

BONUS QUESTION

E1) Deadly.	E1

Sticking words together

Copy out the words once, cover with the flap and write them again.
Get _____ right to become a Spelling Superstar.

Read	Copy	Cover
1) everyone	1	1
2) everybody	2	2
3) everywhere	3	3
4) nobody	4	4
5) nothing	5	5
6) anywhere	6	6
7) anything	7	7
8) someone	8	8
9) somebody	9	9
10) something	10	10
11) upstairs	11	11
12) weekend	12	12
13) breakfast	13	13
14) clockwise	14	14
15) football	15	15
16) grandmother	16	16
17) gunpowder	17	17
18) paintbrush	18	18
19) handshake	19	19
20) bookcase	20	20

BONUS QUESTION		
E1) chambermaid	E1	E1

Sticking words together

Put the flap over the last page and use the hints to work out the words.
Get _____ right to become a Spelling Superstar.

Hint hint

1) All people — 'e _ _ r _ o _ _'.

2) All people — 'e _ _ r _ b _ _ _'.

3) All places.

4) No person.

5) Not anything.

6) In any place.

7) A thing of any kind.

8) A person — 's _ m _ o _ _'.

9) A person — 's _ m _ b _ _ _'.

10) A thing.

11) On a higher floor.

12) Saturday and Sunday.

13) First meal of the day.

14) In the direction of a clock hand.

15) David Beckham plays this game.

16) Your mother's mother.

17) An explosive powder.

18) Artist's brush.

19) Greeting.

20) Storage for books.

One last time...

1 ....

2 ....

3 ....

4 ....

5 ....

6 ....

7 ....

8 ....

9 ....

10 ....

11 ....

12 ....

13 ....

14 ....

15 ....

16 ....

17 ....

18 ....

19 ....

20 ....

BONUS QUESTION

E1) A maid at a hotel.

E1 ....

Sticking words together

Copy out the words once, cover with the flap and write them again.
Get _____ right to become a Spelling Superstar.

Read	Copy	Cover
1) cupboard	1	1
2) windmill	2	2
3) earthworm	3	3
4) bricklayer	4	4
5) blackboard	5	5
6) churchyard	6	6
7) dustbin	7	7
8) playground	8	8
9) deadline	9	9
10) goalkeeper	10	10
11) sideboard	11	11
12) greenhouse	12	12
13) houseplant	13	13
14) pancake	14	14
15) doorframe	15	15
16) mousetrap	16	16
17) footstep	17	17
18) bookshop	18	18
19) keyhole	19	19
20) snowmobile	20	20

BONUS QUESTION		
E1) wishbone	E1	E1

Sticking words together

Put the flap over the last page and use the hints to work out the words.
Get _____ right to become a Spelling Superstar.

Hint hint	One last time...
1) Place for storing things.	1
2) One of these:	2
3) e _ _ _ h _ o _ _	3
4) Someone who builds walls.	4
5) Board for writing on in chalk.	5
6) Grounds around a church.	6
7) What you put rubbish in.	7
8) Place to play in.	8
9) Time limit for finishing something.	9
10) Stops the ball going into the net.	10
11) Dining room cupboard.	11
12) Building made of glass for plants.	12
13) Plant grown inside.	13
14) Eat these on Shrove Tuesday.	14
15) Surrounds a door.	15
16) For catching mice.	16
17) A step taken when walking.	17
18) Where you go to buy books.	18
19) Hole for putting a key into a lock.	19
20) Vehicle for travelling on snow.	20

BONUS QUESTION

E1) Bone by the neck of a bird.	E1

Shortened words

Copy out the words once, cover with the flap and write them again.
Get _____ right to become a Spelling Superstar.

Read	Copy	Cover
1) I'd	1	1
2) I've	2	2
3) it's	3	3
4) I'll	4	4
5) I'm	5	5
6) you're	6	6
7) you've	7	7
8) you'll	8	8
9) you'd	9	9
10) he's	10	10
11) he'll	11	11
12) she's	12	12
13) we're	13	13
14) we'll	14	14
15) we've	15	15
16) we'd	16	16
17) they're	17	17
18) they'll	18	18
19) they've	19	19
20) they'd	20	20
BONUS QUESTION		
E1) who'd	E1	E1

Shortened words

Put the flap over the last page and use the hints to work out the words.
Get _____ right to become a Spelling Superstar.

Hint hint	One last time...
1) I would or I had.	1
2) I have.	2
3) It is.	3
4) I will.	4
5) I am.	5
6) You are.	6
7) You have.	7
8) You will.	8
9) You would or you had.	9
10) He is.	10
11) He will.	11
12) She is.	12
13) We are.	13
14) We will.	14
15) We have.	15
16) We would or we had.	16
17) They are.	17
18) They will.	18
19) They have.	19
20) They would or they had.	20

BONUS QUESTION	
E1) Who would.	E1

Shortened words

Copy out the words once, cover with the flap and write them again.
Get _____ right to become a Spelling Superstar.

Read	Copy	Cover
1) can't	1	1
2) don't	2	2
3) won't	3	3
4) isn't	4	4
5) shan't	5	5
6) doesn't	6	6
7) haven't	7	7
8) aren't	8	8
9) couldn't	9	9
10) weren't	10	10
11) hadn't	11	11
12) wouldn't	12	12
13) shouldn't	13	13
14) o'clock	14	14
15) 'tis	15	15
16) ma'am	16	16
17) salt 'n' vinegar	17	17
18) tell 'em	18	18
19) didn't	19	19
20) it'll	20	20

BONUS QUESTION		
E1) should've	E1	E1

Spelling Book 1 — Combining and Shortening Words © CGP 2002

Shortened words

Put the flap over the last page and use the hints to work out the words.
Get _____ right to become a Spelling Superstar.

Hint hint	One last time...
1) Cannot.	1
2) Do not.	2
3) Will not.	3
4) Is not.	4
5) Shall not.	5
6) Does not.	6
7) Have not.	7
8) Are not.	8
9) Could not.	9
10) Were not.	10
11) Had not.	11
12) Would not.	12
13) Should not.	13
14) The hour of, e.g. 5 _ ' _ _ _ _ _.	14
15) It is (old-fashioned).	15
16) Madam.	16
17) Salt and vinegar.	17
18) Tell them.	18
19) Did not.	19
20) It will.	20

BONUS QUESTION	
E1) Should have.	E1

Silent letters

Copy out the words once, cover with the flap and write them again.
Get _____ right to become a Spelling Superstar.

Read	Copy	Cover
1) would	1	1
2) knuckle	2	2
3) gnash	3	3
4) wrapper	4	4
5) whine	5	5
6) lamb	6	6
7) knock	7	7
8) know	8	8
9) knight	9	9
10) gnarled	10	10
11) wrong	11	11
12) sword	12	12
13) salmon	13	13
14) folk	14	14
15) doubt	15	15
16) rhino	16	16
17) gnat	17	17
18) debt	18	18
19) answer	19	19
20) kneel	20	20

BONUS QUESTION		
E1) chemist	E1	E1

Silent letters

38

Put the flap over the last page and use the hints to work out the words.
Get _____ right to become a Spelling Superstar.

Hint hint	One last time...
1) I _ _ _ _ _ if I could.	1
2) Finger joint.	2
3) Grind your teeth.	3
4) Covering.	4
5) Long, high-pitched note.	5
6) Young sheep.	6
7) Do this on a door before entering.	7
8) Be aware of.	8
9) Brave 'Sir'.	9
10) Twisted and knobbly.	10
11) Not right.	11
12) Long knife.	12
13) Type of fish.	13
14) People.	14
15) Not being sure of something.	15
16) One of these:	16
17) Biting insect.	17
18) Something that you owe.	18
19) Response to a question.	19
20) Bend your leg.	20

BONUS QUESTION

E1) Type of scientist.	E1

© CGP 2002

Year Three Spelling — Tricky Words

More silent letters

Copy out the words once, cover with the flap and write them again.
Get _____ right to become a Spelling Superstar.

Read	Copy	Cover
1) knee	1	1
2) gnome	2	2
3) rhyme	3	3
4) rhubarb	4	4
5) numb	5	5
6) calf	6	6
7) knit	7	7
8) wrinkle	8	8
9) gnaw	9	9
10) calm	10	10
11) bomb	11	11
12) thumb	12	12
13) write	13	13
14) wrist	14	14
15) whale	15	15
16) whirl	16	16
17) plumb	17	17
18) chalk	18	18
19) wheat	19	19
20) knot	20	20

BONUS QUESTION		
E1) crumb	E1	E1

More silent letters

Put the flap over the last page and use the hints to work out the words.
Get _____ right to become a Spelling Superstar.

Hint hint	One last time...
1) Leg joint.	1
2) Garden ornament.	2
3) Sound the same.	3
4) Sweet, red-stalked vegetable.	4
5) Without any feeling.	5
6) Young cow.	6
7) Make out of wool.	7
8) Small crease in the skin.	8
9) Chew on, nibble.	9
10) Peaceful.	10
11) Weapon that explodes.	11
12) First digit on the hand.	12
13) Put words on paper.	13
14) Joint between hand and arm.	14
15) Sea mammal.	15
16) Spin round.	16
17) Fit water pipes.	17
18) Powdery stick for writing with.	18
19) Grain used to make bread.	19
20) Tie ropes together with one.	20

BONUS QUESTION

E1) Very small piece of bread.	E1

More than one meaning

Copy out the words once, cover with the flap and write them again.
Get _____ right to become a Spelling Superstar.

Read	Copy	Cover
1) flat	1	1
2) watch	2	2
3) crane	3	3
4) club	4	4
5) plain	5	5
6) last	6	6
7) wave	7	7
8) yard	8	8
9) float	9	9
10) letter	10	10
11) warm	11	11
12) tug	12	12
13) bank	13	13
14) form	14	14
15) stand	15	15
16) ring	16	16
17) bat	17	17
18) spot	18	18
19) race	19	19
20) gum	20	20

BONUS QUESTION		
E1) lead	E1	E1

Spelling Book 1 — Tricky Words

More than one meaning

Put the flap over the last page and use the hints to work out the words.
Get _____ right to become a Spelling Superstar.

Hint hint	One last time...
1) Not bumpy.	1
2) Look at carefully.	2
3) Type of water bird.	3
4) One of these: ♣	4
5) Clear and simple.	5
6) Final one.	6
7) Raise hand in greeting.	7
8) Old measurement of length.	8
9) Be held up by water.	9
10) There are 26 in the alphabet.	10
11) Neither hot nor cold.	11
12) Pull.	12
13) Place to keep money.	13
14) Application _ _ _ _.	14
15) Be upright on your feet.	15
16) Round piece of jewellery.	16
17) Flying mammal.	17
18) Blemish.	18
19) Running competition.	19
20) Chewing _ _ _.	20

BONUS QUESTION

E1) A heavy metal.	E1

More than one meaning

Copy out the words once, cover with the flap and write them again.
Get _____ right to become a Spelling Superstar.

Read	Copy	Cover
1) dear	1	1
2) jam	2	2
3) grate	3	3
4) snap	4	4
5) sound	5	5
6) foot	6	6
7) train	7	7
8) sharp	8	8
9) fine	9	9
10) slide	10	10
11) table	11	11
12) light	12	12
13) safe	13	13
14) arms	14	14
15) rose	15	15
16) pop	16	16
17) stick	17	17
18) row	18	18
19) book	19	19
20) fit	20	20

BONUS QUESTION		
E1) catch	E1	E1

More than one meaning

Copy out the words once, cover with the flap and write them again.
Get _____ right to become a Spelling Superstar.

Hint hint	One last time...
1) Expensive.	1
2) Fruit preserve.	2
3) Fireplace.	3
4) Break.	4
5) Noise.	5
6) Thing at the end of your leg.	6
7) Transport that runs on rails.	7
8) With a cutting edge.	8
9) Good quality, excellent.	9
10) Playground ride.	10
11) Piece of furniture with a flat top.	11
12) Not dark.	12
13) Not dangerous.	13
14) Limbs with hands on the end.	14
15) A romantic flower.	15
16) Popular music.	16
17) S _ _ _ _ like glue.	17
18) Use an oar.	18
19) Something you read.	19
20) _ _ _ and healthy.	20

BONUS QUESTION

E1) Don't drop.	E1

© CGP 2002   1010 - 8467   *Year Three Spelling — Tricky Words*

Keep out of reach of small teachers

ISBN 978 1 84146 167 0

9 781841 461670

E3S21

£ 3·50

www.cgpbooks.co.uk

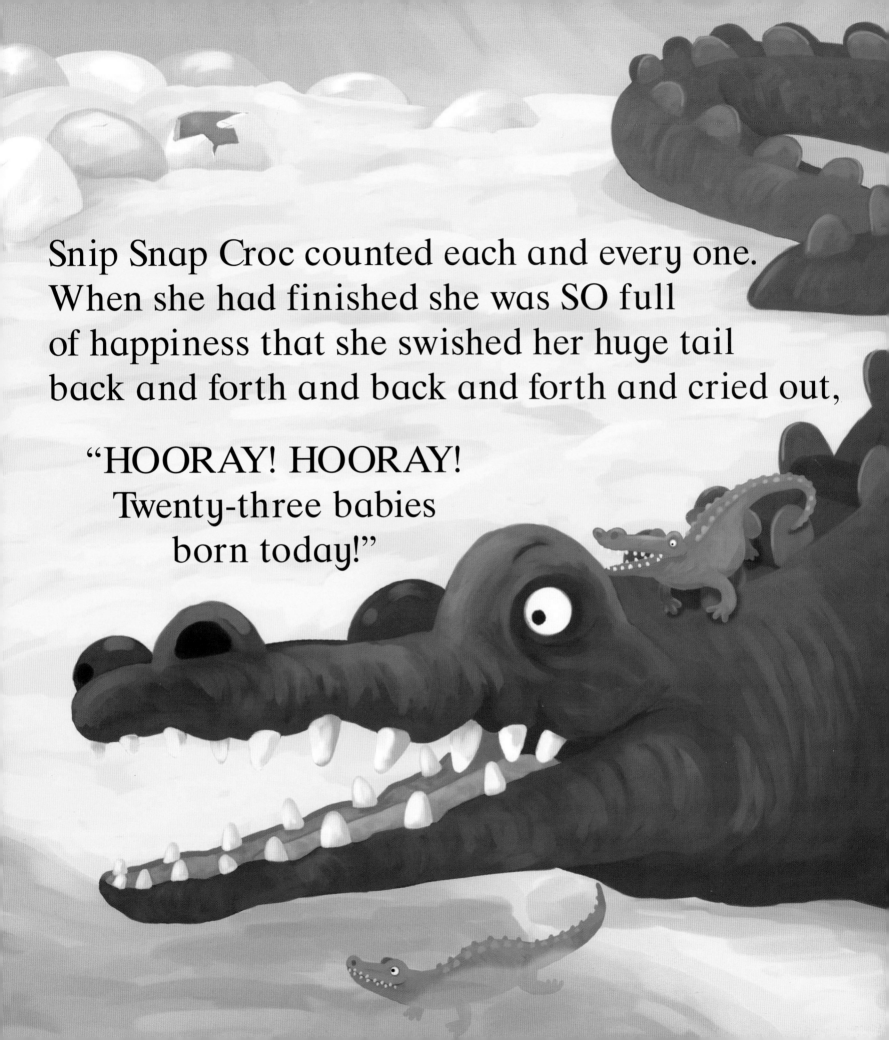

Snip Snap Croc counted each and every one.
When she had finished she was SO full
of happiness that she swished her huge tail
back and forth and back and forth and cried out,

"HOORAY! HOORAY!
Twenty-three babies
born today!"

Baby Baboon, the baby meerkats and the two little lion cubs watched from the safety of the riverbank.

They could not believe their eyes. One by one, Snip Snap Croc popped each baby into her mouth!

"Oh, Mama, come quick!" cried Baby Baboon.

"Oh, Mama, over here!" cried the baby meerkats.

"Oh, Mama," cried the lion cubs, "Just *look*!"

Then Snip Snap Croc called out,
"All riverbank creatures, listen to me:
Stay away from my babies twenty-three.
Or by the sky above and the earth beneath,
I will snap you up with my big, sharp teeth."

Mama Snip Snap Croc told her babies,
"Don't stray far from your Mama Croc,
For there are creatures who would eat *you* up.
Stay close by me and no harm you'll meet.
For I love you more than the river deep."

And Mama Baboon, Mama Meerkat and Mama Lion all sighed happily. They knew that although Snip Snap Croc was fierce and dangerous, she wanted to keep her babies safe, just as they did their own.

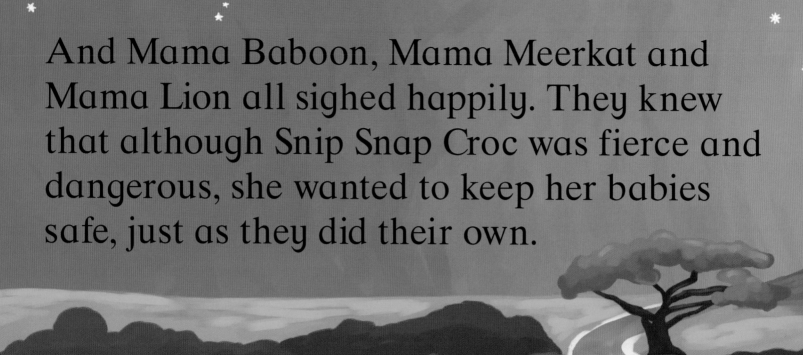

And they knew she loved each and every one, just as much as they did their own.

Mountain high,

Star bright,

Ocean wide...
and river deep.

Notes For Teachers and Parents

- Look at the front cover of the book together. Talk about the picture. Can the children guess what the book is going to be about? Read the title together.

- When the children first read the story (or had it read to them), how did they think it was going to end? Were they right? How else could the story have ended?

- Ask the children to take it in turns to try to read the story aloud. Help them with any difficult words and remember to praise the children for their efforts in reading the book.

- Spell out the names of the animals in the book. Ask the children to repeat the spellings each time you read the story together.

- The children can then try and think of words that rhyme with the animals' names. Make lists of these rhyming words.

- Encourage the children to write a short poem about one of the animals. Use your rhyming word lists to help.

- With the children, make up a tune and sing a verse of one of the mother animals' rhymes.

- Play a game thinking how big, deep, high, loud, etc, love could be. What do all the animals' mums have in common? Discuss how all mums, even the most fierce, love and protect their babies. Encourage the children to talk about what kinds of things their mums (or other carers) do to protect them.

- Study a map of the River Nile with the children and choose where Snip Snap Croc might live. This is a good opportunity to talk about Africa. Explain that Africa is a continent and how continents are usually divided into different countries. Can the children name any other continents? Do they know which continent they live in?

- Make a collage of the river and its surroundings. Ask the children to make individual drawings or paintings of Snip Snap Croc and the other animals in the story. These can then be glued onto the collage. Discuss what other animals may live in the area – for example, giraffe, pelican, eagle, hippopotamus.